NEW BIG FUN 3

WORKBOOK

Mario Herrera
Barbara Hojel

New Big Fun
Workbook 3 with Audio CD
Pearson Education Limited

KAO Two, KAO Park, Harlow, Essex CM179NA, England and Associated Companies throughout the world.
www.English.com
© Pearson Education Limited 2018

The right of Mario Herrera and Barbara Hojel to be identified as authors of this Work has been asserted by them in accordance with the Copyright, Designs and Patents Act 1988.
All rights reserved; no part of this publication may be reproduced, stored in a retrieval system, or transmitted in any form or by any means, electronic, mechanical, photocopying, recording, or otherwise without the prior written permission of the Publishers

First published 2018

ISBN: 978-1-2922-6575-9

Set in Gill Sans Infant Std, Avenir LT Pro, ITC Avant Garde Gothic Std, Banco ITC Font

Printed in China (GCC/01)

Text composition: Isabel Arnaud
Illustration credits: A Corazón Abierto, Javier Montiel

PEARSON ELT ON THE WEB

PearsonELT.com offers a wide range of classroom resources and professional development materials. Access course-specific websites, product information, and Pearson offices around the world.

Visit us at **www.pearsonELT.com**.

CONTENTS

1. **My School** 1
2. **My Senses** 11
3. **My Family** 21
4. **My Toys** 31
5. **Food** 41
6. **My Clothes** 51
7. **Animals** 61
8. **My World** 71
9. **Show Time!** 81

NEW BIG FUN Song

From the sky to the ground
And all the way around—
We can have big fun!
If there's rain, if there's sun,
Let's play with everyone.
We can have big, big fun!

Chorus →

Take a walk outside.
Our world is big and wide.
There are flowers and trees
And yellow bumblebees.
Buzz, buzz, buzz!

(Chorus)

Join your hands with me.
Let's see what we can see!
Then take a closer look.
We'll learn beyond our book.
Look, oh, look!

(Chorus)

1 AT SCHOOL

What is wrong? Find and circle.

Draw the English teacher and the principal.

Vocabulary Practice: *English teacher, music teacher, principal, secretary*

Look and match.

Vocabulary Practice: *gym teacher, janitor, gatekeeper*

✂ **Cut out and paste. Draw yourself and color.**

Vocabulary Review: *bus driver, music teacher, bus, classroom*

Look and circle the correct letter. Trace and draw.

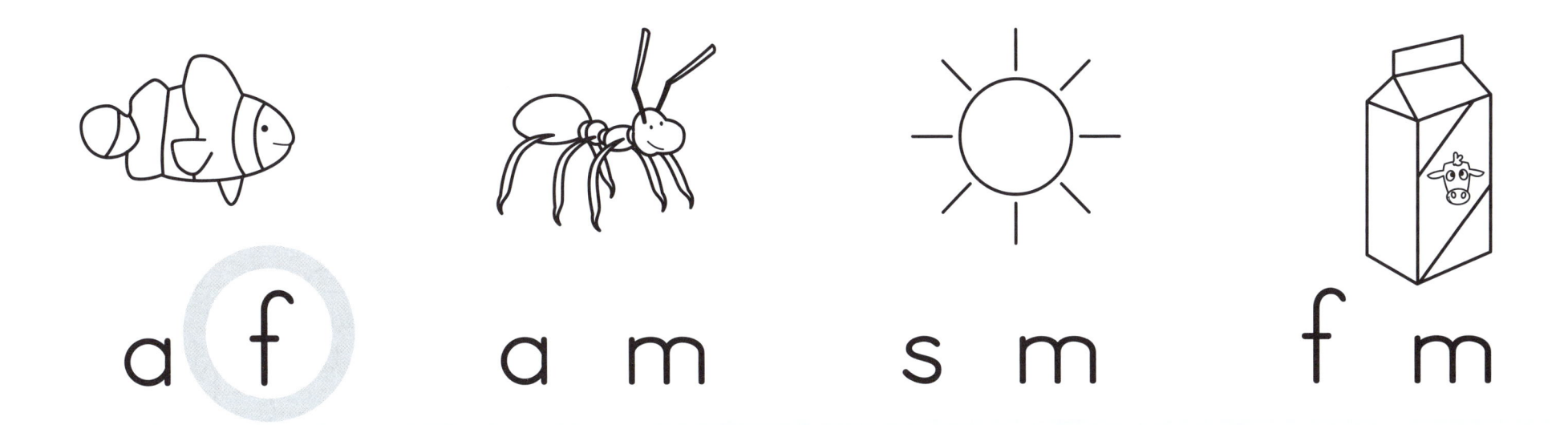

a (f)   a m   s m   f m

Ff   Aa   Ss   Mm

Pre-reading and Pre-writing Practice: *Ff, Aa, Ss, Mm*

VALUES

Look, trace, and draw a happy face or a sad face.

6 Values: We respect others.

Listen and point. Listen again, match, and trace the numbers.

Who Is She?

1   2   3   4

Story Sequence: *Who Is She?*

Count, draw, and trace. Color.

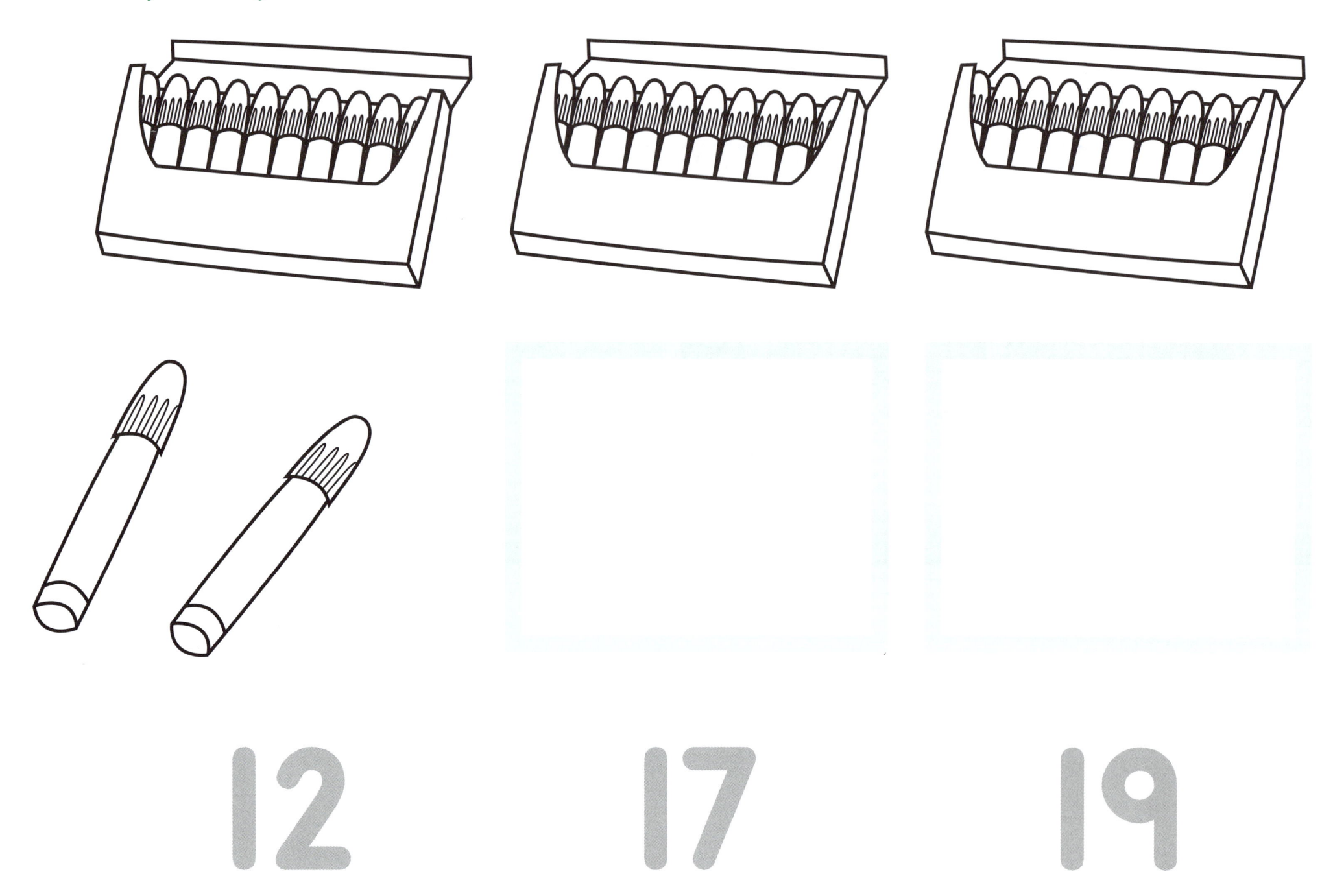

12   17   19

Math Practice: *Numbers 1–19*; sets of 10

What does each animal make? Look and match. Color.

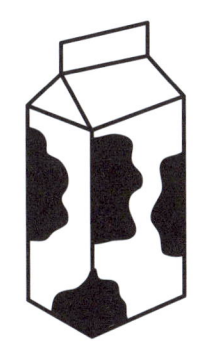

AMAZING

Amazing: Science Connection: cow, milk, bee, honey, chicken, eggs, sheep, wool

AT SCHOOL

Draw people at school.

10 Personal Response

2 FEELINGS

What is wrong? Find and circle.

Opener 11

Look and color the matching face.

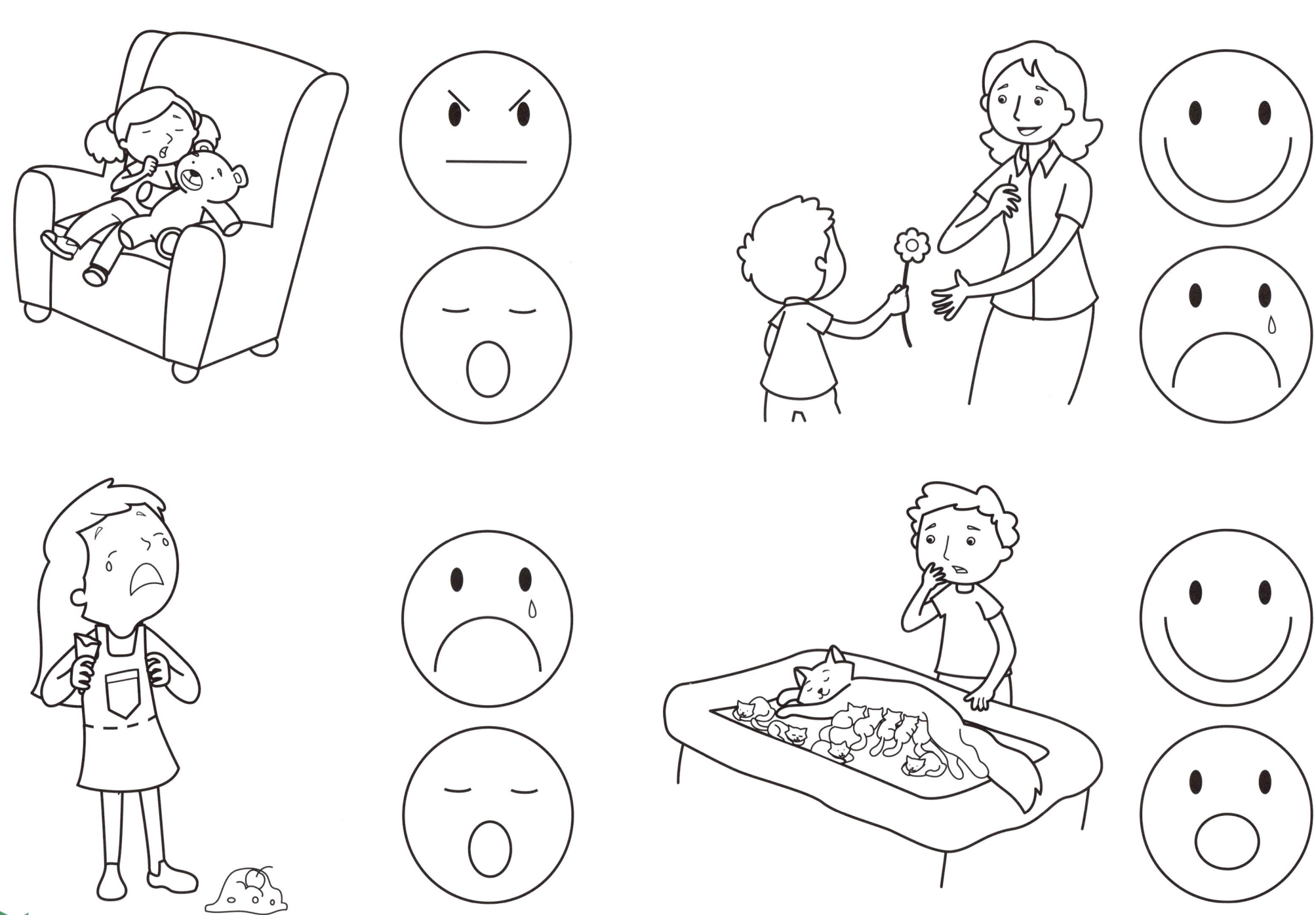

Vocabulary Practice: *sleepy, happy, sad, amazed*

Look and match.

Vocabulary Practice: scared, mad, sick, excited

Trace and draw actions that make Mom mad and happy.

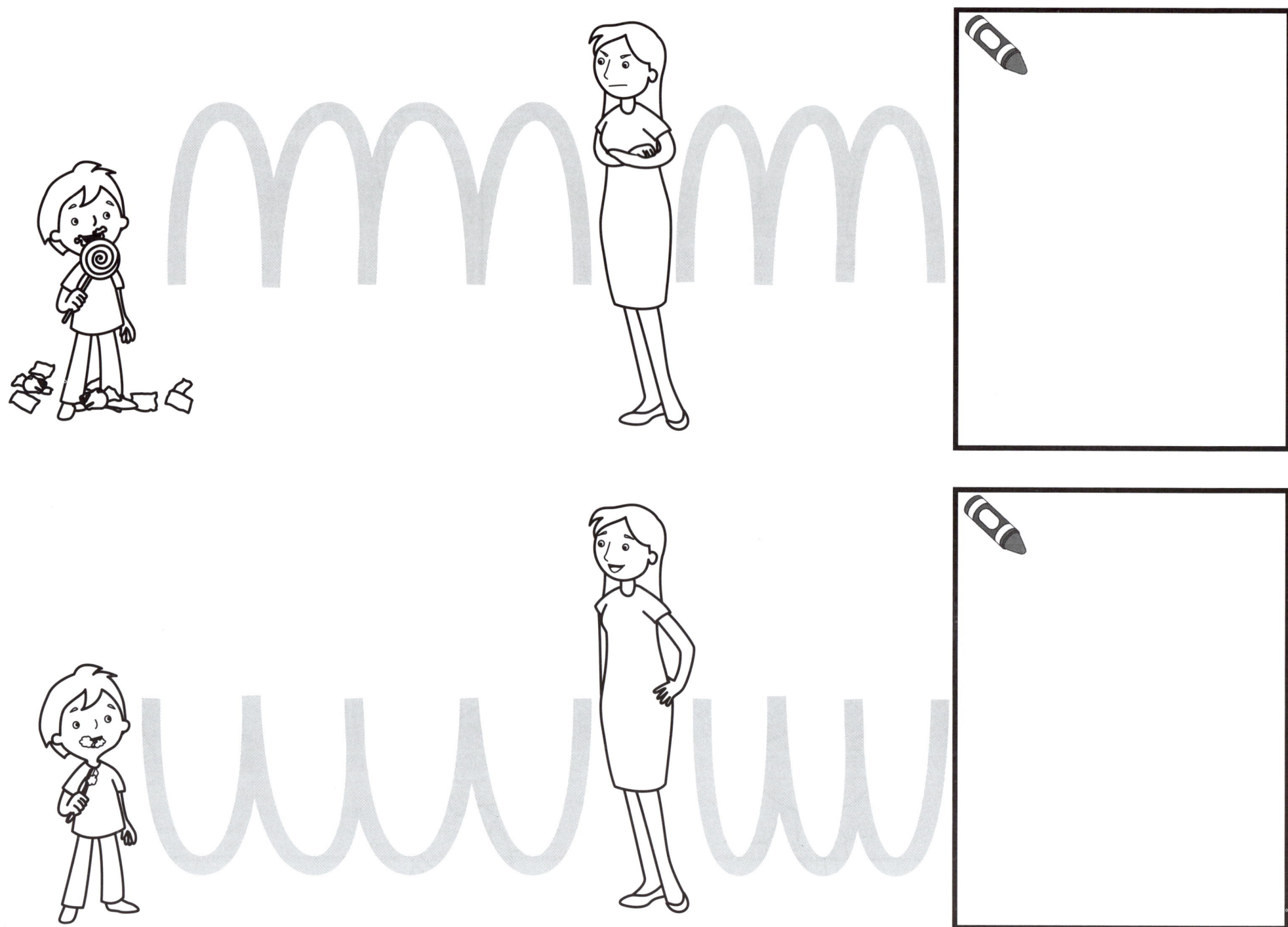

Vocabulary Practice: *eat unhealthy food, brush my teeth; mad, happy*

Look and circle the correct letter. Trace and draw.

I t   p l   e t   e p

T t   L l   E e   P p

VALUES

Who is staying healthy? Color the frame. Draw.

How do you stay healthy?

Values: We stay healthy.

Cut out, listen, and paste.

Are You Okay?

1

2

3

4

Story Sequence: *Are You Okay?*

Color the faces and count. Trace the number.

23 27 29

18 Math Practice: *Numbers 20–29*

Look and circle the parts of the animals' bodies that protect them.

Amazing: Science Connection: *owl, claws; rhinoceros, horns; tiger, fangs/claws*

FEELINGS

Draw your feelings.

3 HOME

What is wrong? Find and circle.

Where are the family members? Look and match.

Vocabulary Practice and Review: family members; *living room, bedroom, bathroom, kitchen*

✂ Cut out and paste. Say.

Vocabulary Practice: *dining room, hallway, closet, stairs*
Language Practice: *Where is (the cat)? It's (in the closet).*

UNIT 3
23

What is missing in each room? Trace, draw, and color.

24 Vocabulary Practice and Review: *kitchen, sink, stove, fridge, bedroom, bed, lamp, closet*

Trace and match.

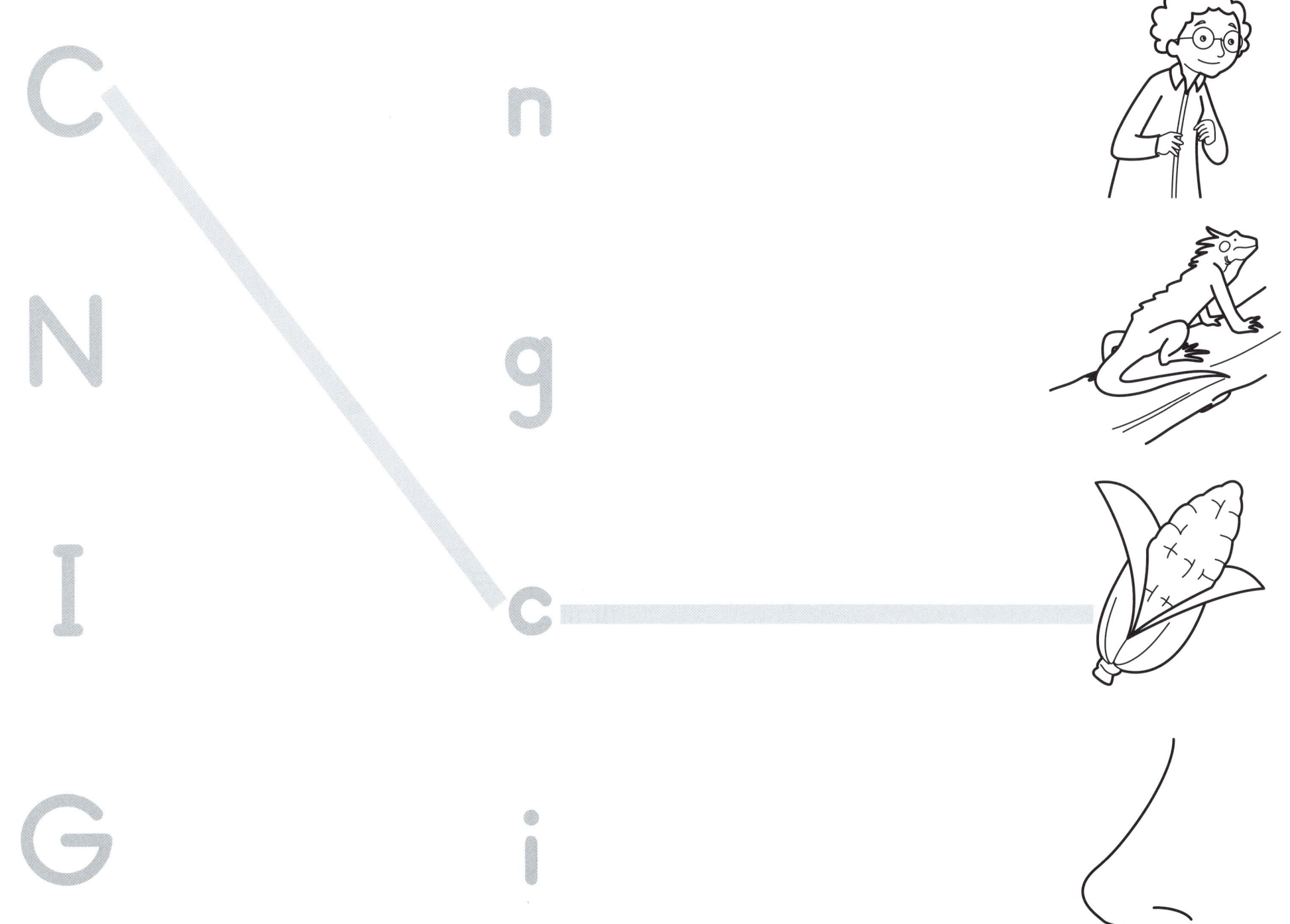

C n

N g

I c

G i

Pre-reading and Pre-writing Practice: *Cc, Nn, Ii, Gg*, and discriminating sounds

VALUES

Are they respecting differences? Complete the face. Trace and read the sentences.

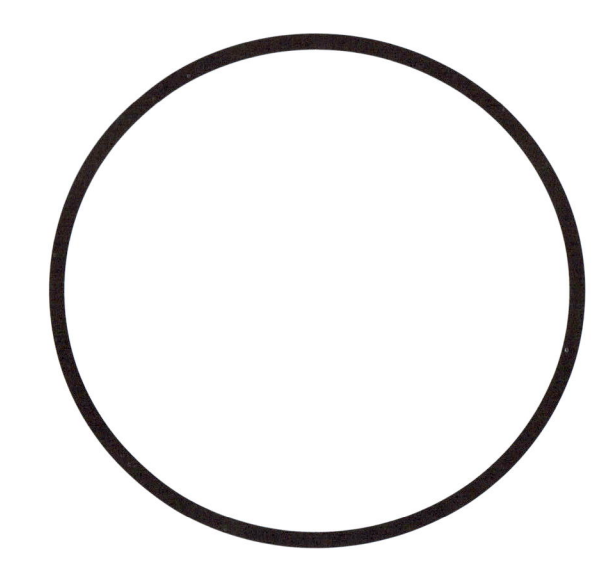

It is a 🪑.

It is a 🍴.

Pre-reading and Pre-writing Practice: Rebuses and simple sentences; *table, fork*
Values: We respect differences.

Look and listen. Draw someone hiding in the box and say.

Where Is Meg?

Where is ... ?

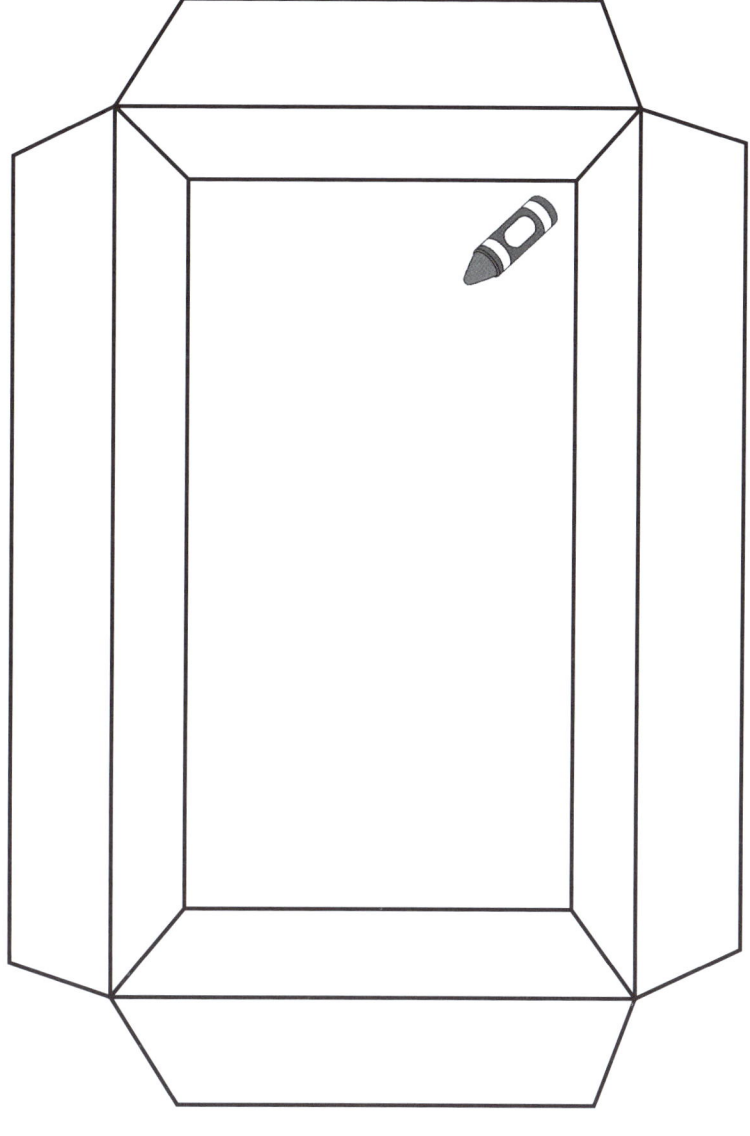

Story Sequence: *Where Is Meg?*

Circle the sets of ten, count and write.

35

39

Math Practice: Numbers 30–39; sets of 10

What is for dinner? Circle an insect and draw it in the spider's web.

AMAZING

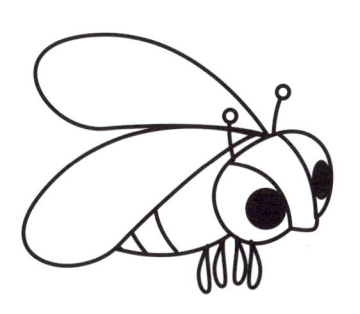

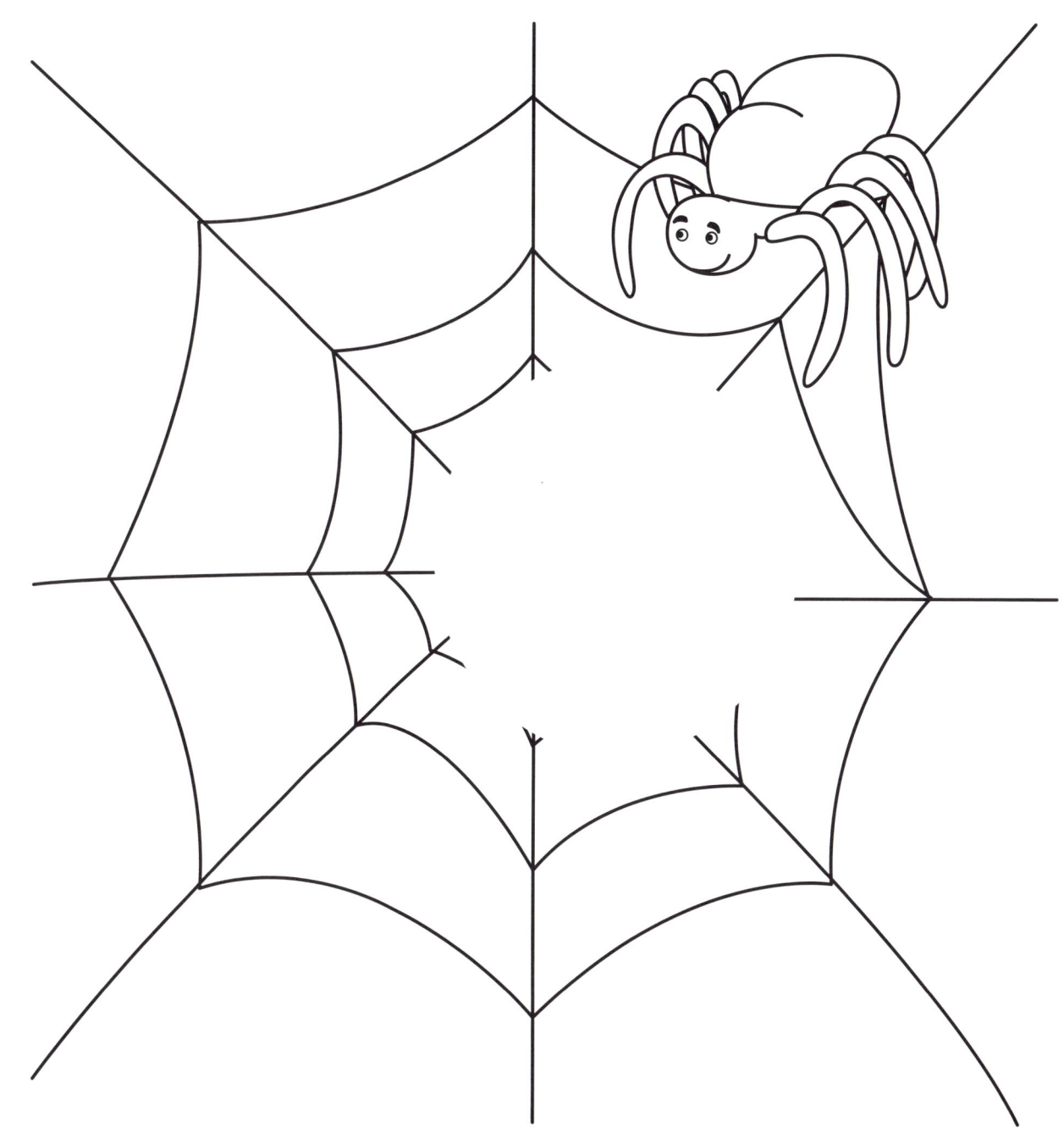

Amazing: Science Connection: *spider, web, butterfly, bee, fly*

UNIT 3
29

HOME

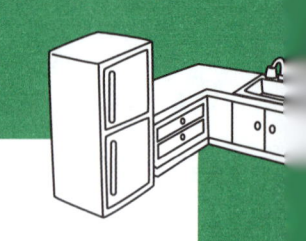

Draw your favorite place at home.

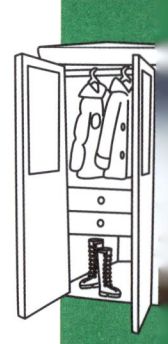

4 RECYCLE

What is wrong? Find and circle.

What do you need to make a wagon? Look and circle or cross out.

Vocabulary Practice: *tape, paper plates, box, string*

What do you need to make a kite? Cut out and paste.

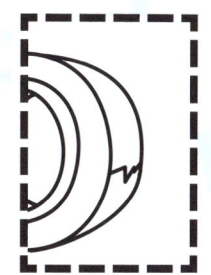

Vocabulary Practice: *paint, paintbrush, sticks, glue*
Vocabulary Review: *paper, tape, string*

Look and color the crayons and the lion mask.

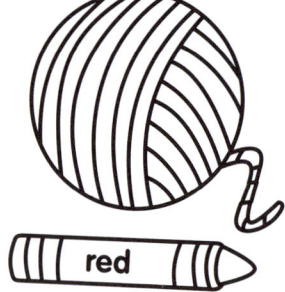

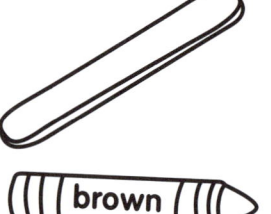

red   yellow   brown

Vocabulary Practice: *paper plate, string, stick*; colors

Trace and write. Trace, read, and circle. Trace, read, and draw.

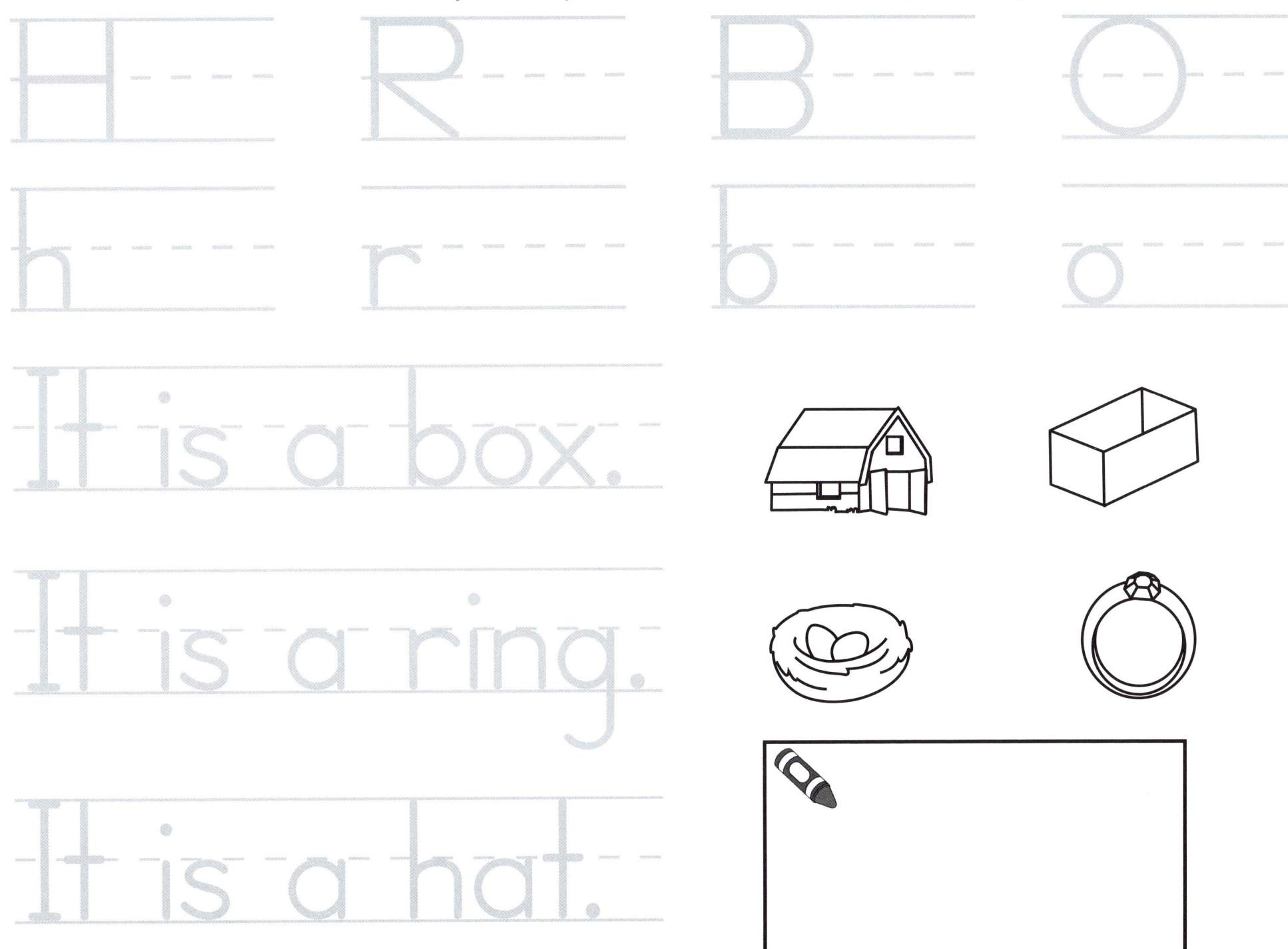

H   R   B   O

h   r   b   o

It is a box.

It is a ring.

It is a hat.

Pre-reading and Pre-writing Practice: *Hh*, *Rr*, *Bb*, *Oo*; simple sentences

UNIT 4
35

VALUES Is he being wasteful? Draw a happy or a sad face. Then draw yourself and complete the face.

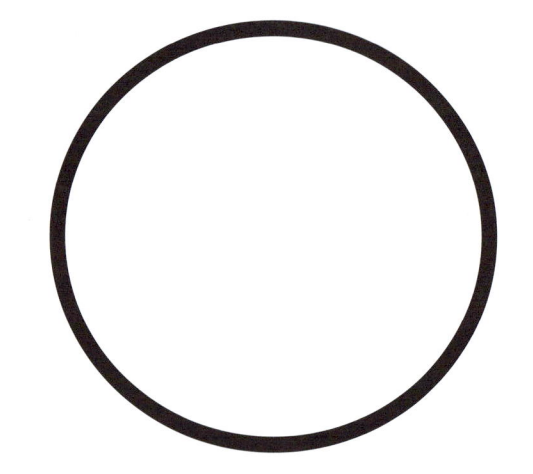

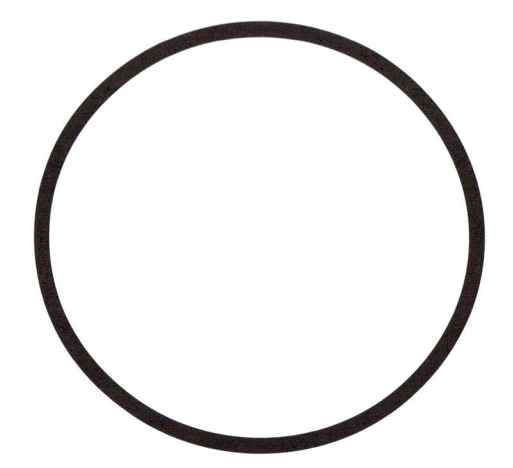

What about you?

Values: We don't waste things.

Look and listen. Color what they need to make a tent.
We Need Books!

What do they need?

Story Sequence: *We Need Books!*

Circle the houses and draw the missing boxes. Color.

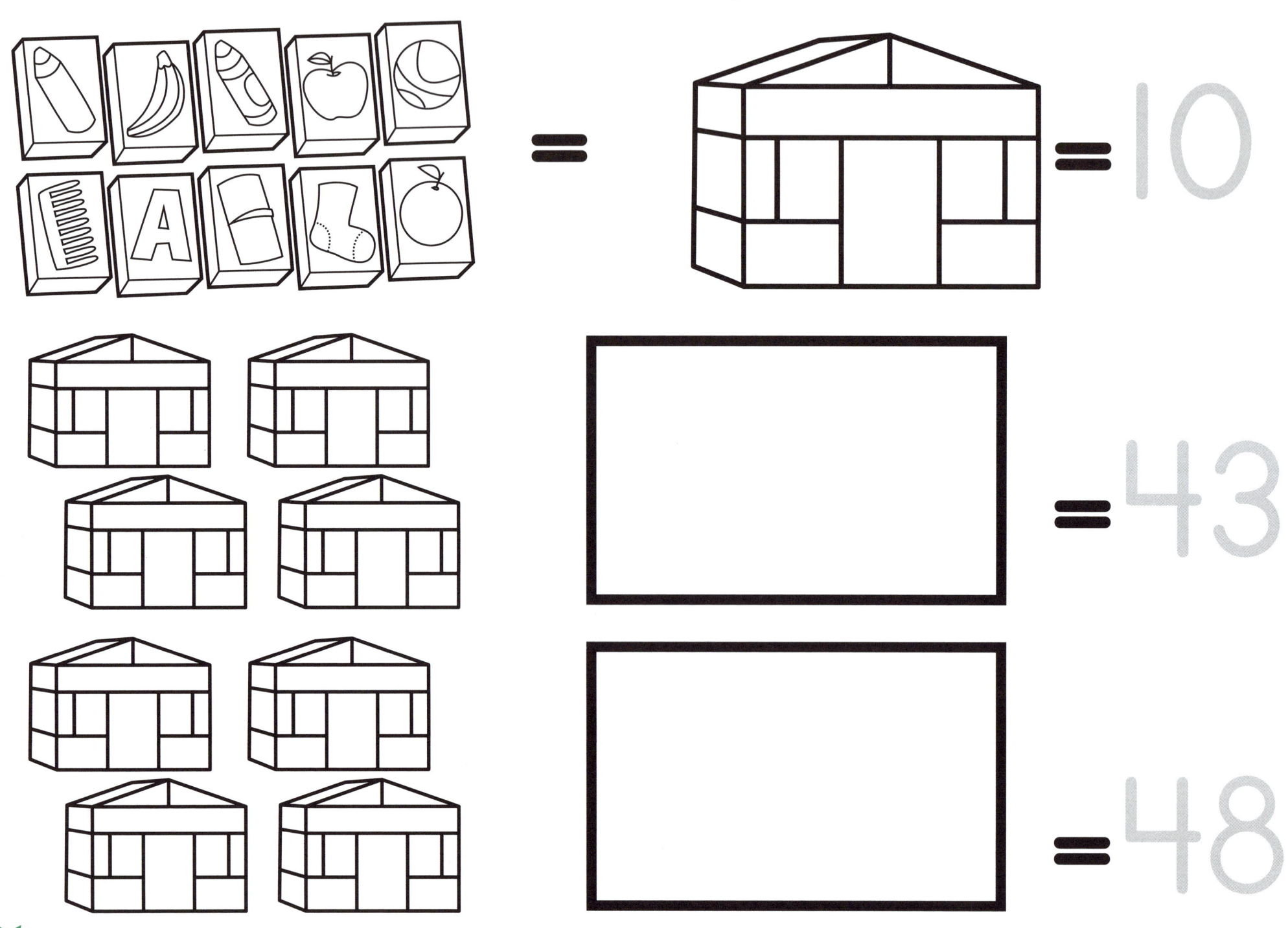

= = 10

= 43

= 48

Math Practice: *Numbers 40–49*; sets of 10

Trace around the flying seeds. Match and color.

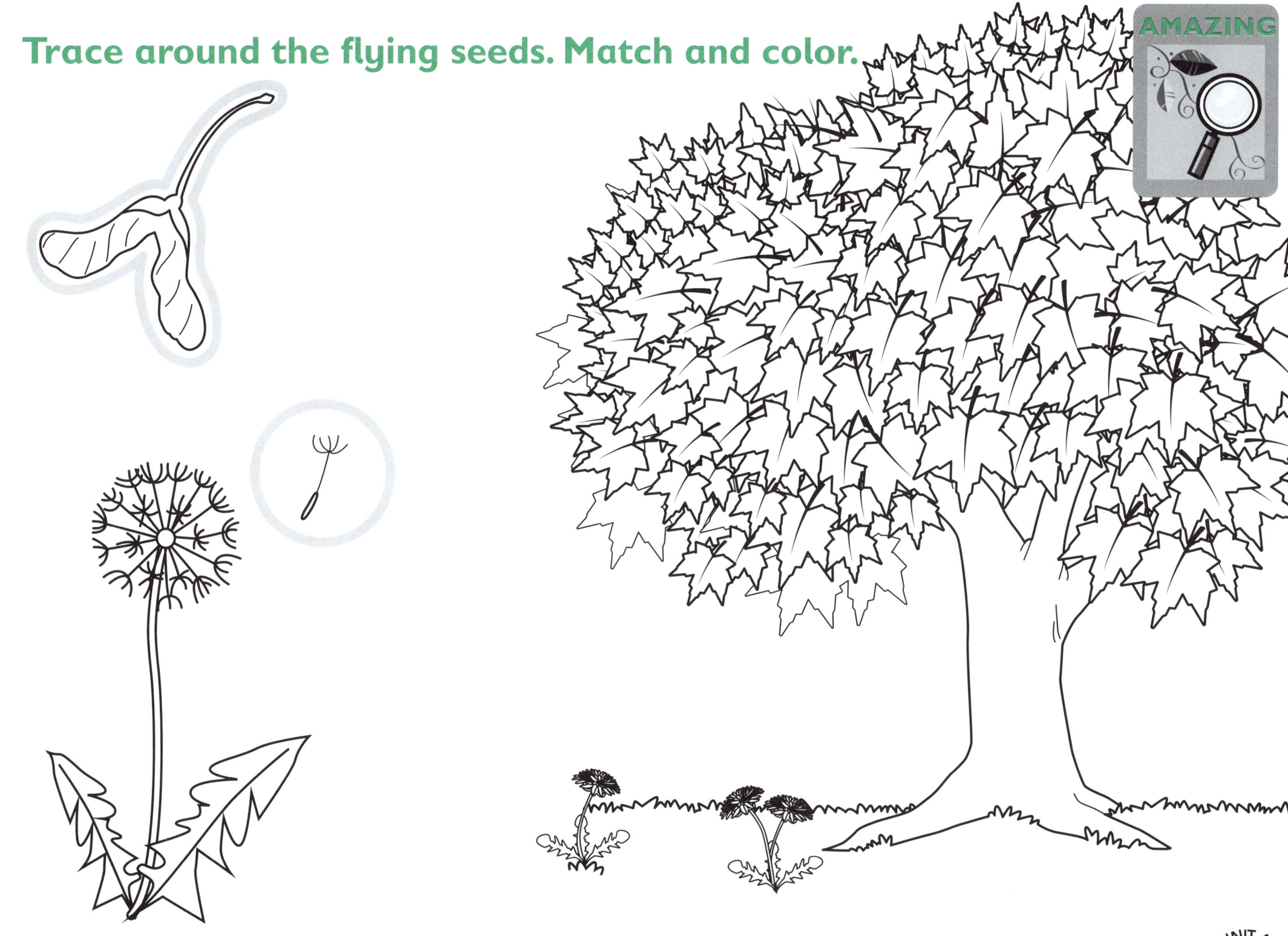

AMAZING

Amazing: Science Connection: *seeds, flowers, tree*

UNIT 4
39

RECYCLE

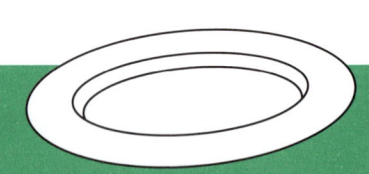

Draw how you recycle.

5 EATING OUT

What is wrong? Find and circle.

What is each person missing? Look and match.

42 Vocabulary Practice: *menu, water, napkin, straw*

✂ **Cut out and paste. Color.**

Vocabulary Practice: *pizza, ice cream, cake, spaghetti*

UNIT 5
43

What do you want to eat and drink? Draw and say.

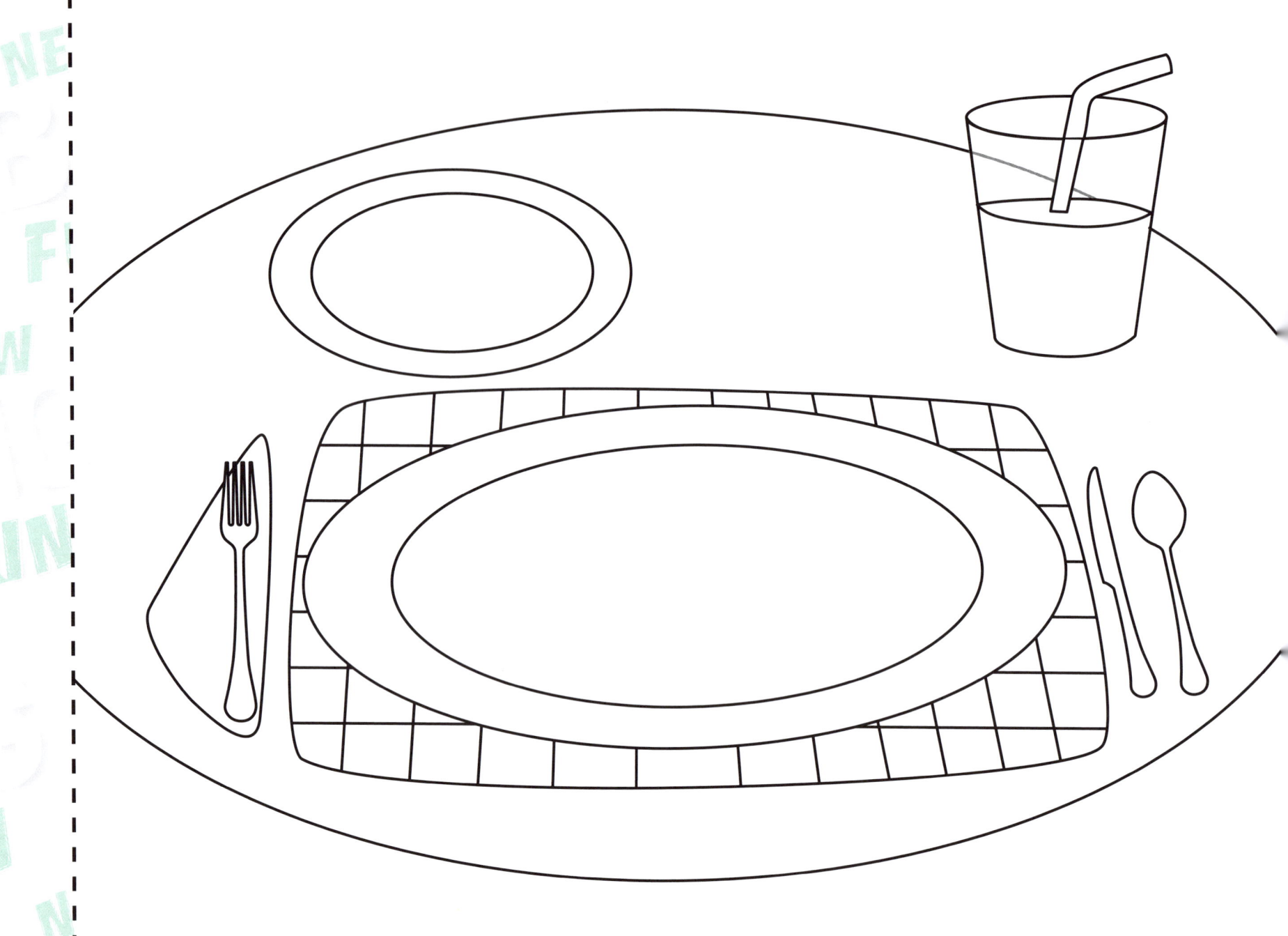

Vocabulary Practice and Review: food; drinks; *napkin, straw*

Trace and match. Trace, write, and read.

K   D   U   J

j   d   k   u

It is a _uck.

It is a _acket.

Pre-reading and Pre-writing Practice: *Kk, Dd, Uu, Jj*; simple sentences

VALUES

Who is helping others? Color the frame. Draw.

What about you?

46 Values: We help each other.

Look and listen. Color the food that Grandma orders.

Lunch with Grandma

What does Grandma order?

Story Sequence: *Lunch with Grandma*

UNIT 5

Count the seeds, trace and color.

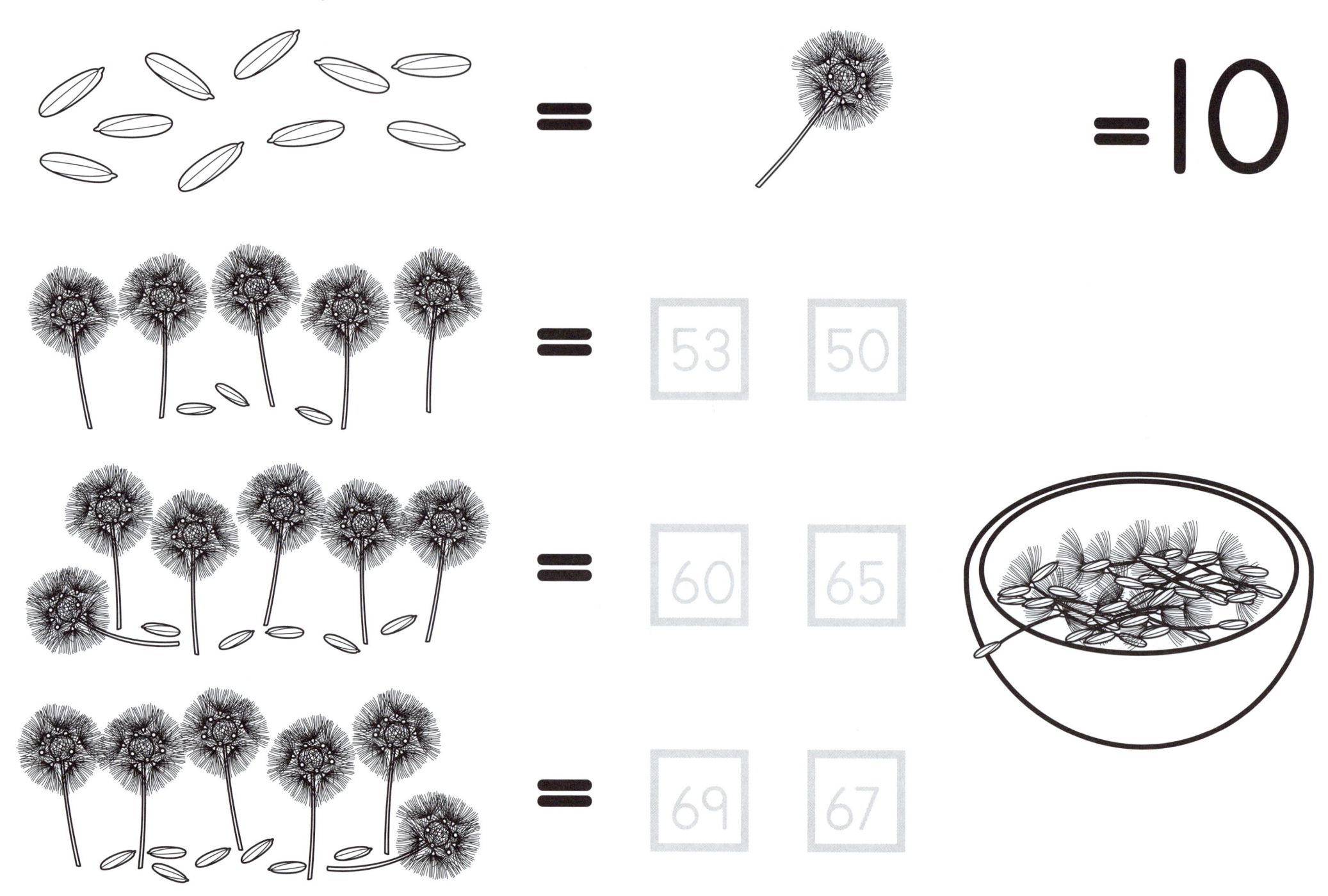

= = 10

= 53 50

= 60 65

= 69 67

Math Practice: Numbers 50–69; sets of 10

Look at the patterns in the fruit and vegetables. Match.

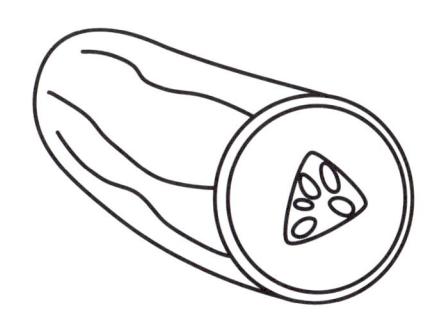

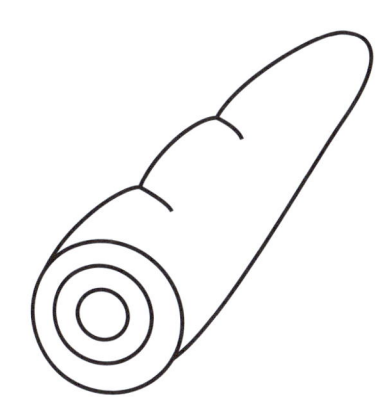

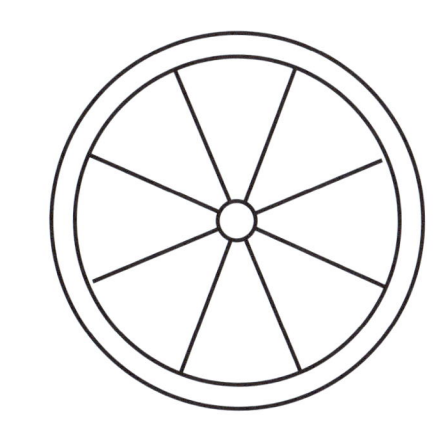

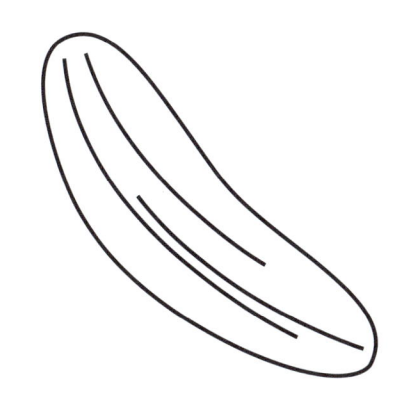

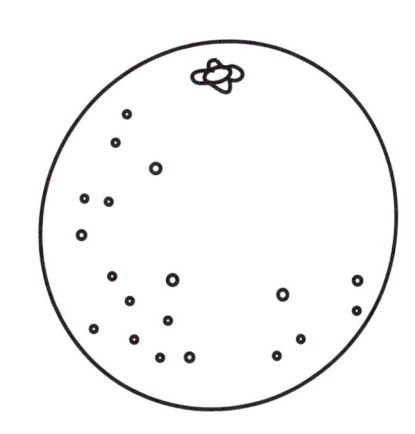

AMAZING

Amazing: Science Connection: *patterns*

UNIT 5
49

EATING OUT

Draw your favorite restaurant.

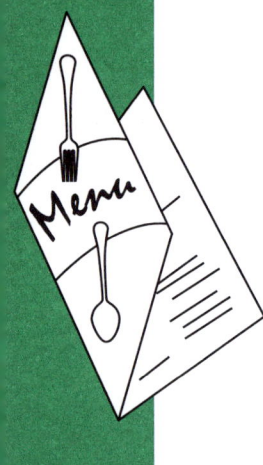

Personal Response

6 OUR THINGS

What is wrong? Find and circle.

Opener
UNIT 6
51

What is each person missing? Look and match.

52 Vocabulary Practice: *tablet, laptop, backpack, cell phone*

Look and circle the differences.

Vocabulary Practice: *necktie, hat, necklace, ring*

Trace, read, and color the corresponding item.

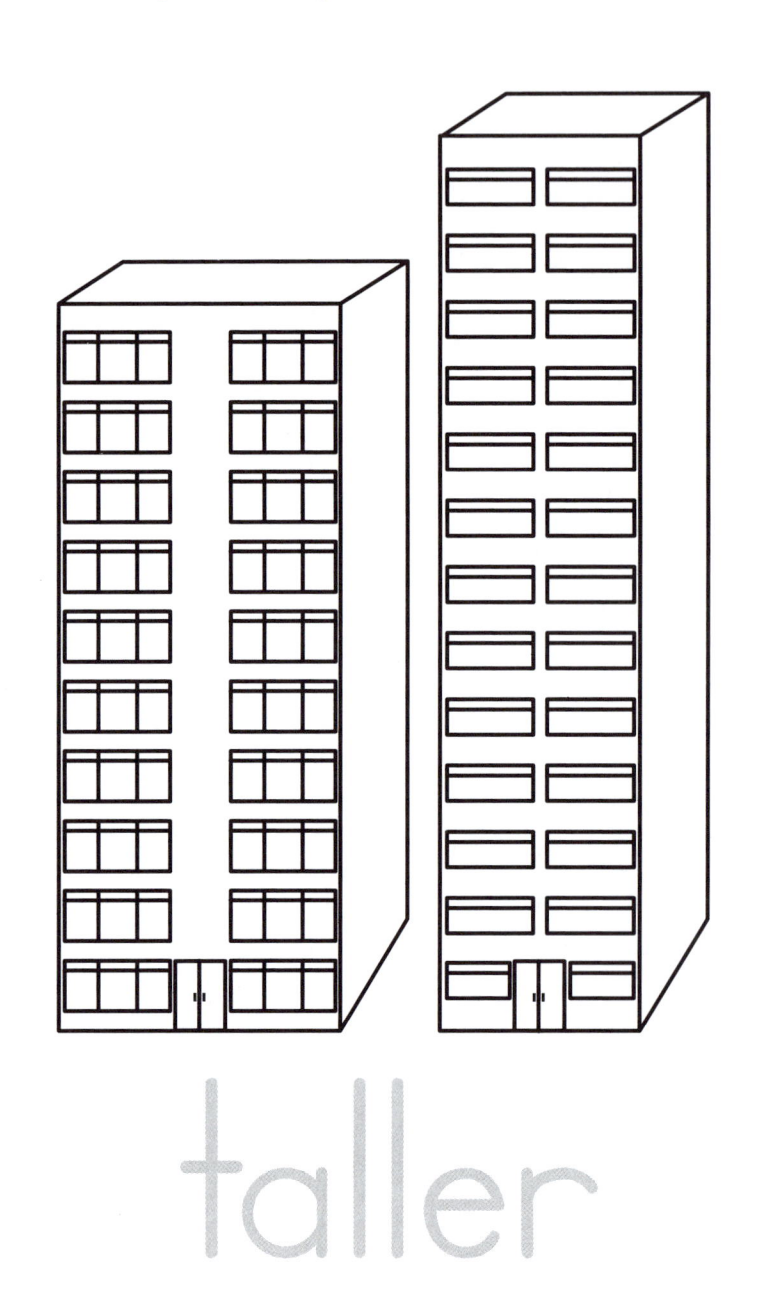

bigger

taller

longer

Trace and match. Then trace, read, and color.

Q   Y   V   W

y   q   w   v

It is a red ⬚.

It is a yellow ⬚.

Pre-reading and Pre-writing Practice: *Qq, Vv, Yy, Ww*; rebuses and simple sentences

VALUES

Is she being neat? Look and draw a happy or a sad face. Then draw yourself and complete the face.

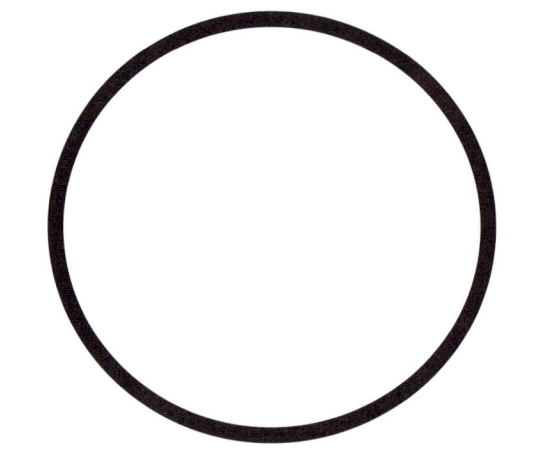

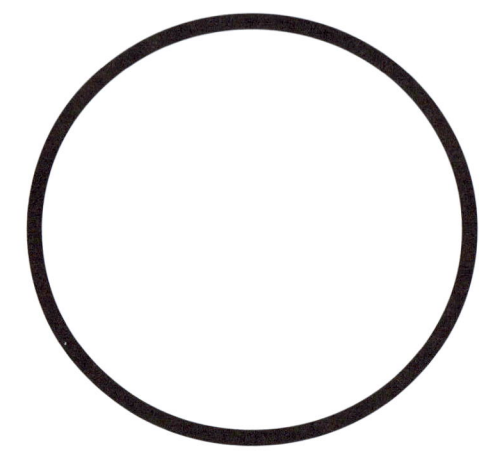

What about you?

Values: We are neat.

Cut out, listen, and paste.

At the Store

1

2

3

4

Story Sequence: *At the Store*

Complete the number line. Count and answer.

70 71 __ 73 74 75 __ 77 __ 79
80 __ 82 83 __ 85 86 __ 88 89

◯ = 10

How many beads? ___

Look and color by number.

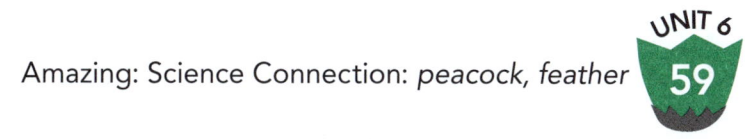

1 brown 2 green
3 blue   4 orange

Amazing: Science Connection: *peacock, feather*

OUR THINGS

Draw your favorite things.

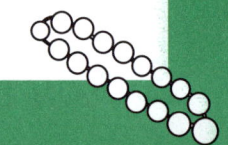

Personal Response

7 ANIMALS

What is wrong? Find and circle.

Look and match.

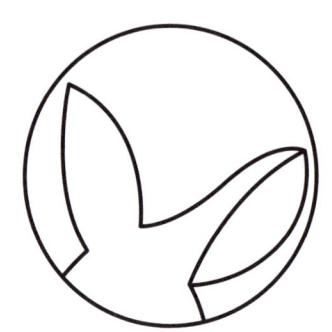

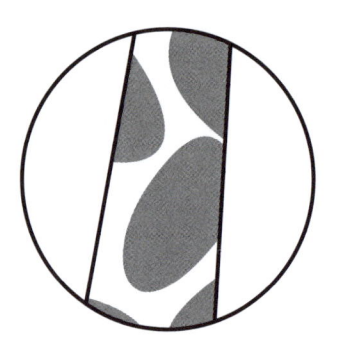

Vocabulary Practice: tigers, seals, giraffes, kangaroos

✂ **Cut out and paste.**

Vocabulary Practice: *monkeys, zebras, elephants, lions; sleeping, eating, playing, running*

UNIT 7
63

Look and draw the morning, afternoon, and night sky. Then say what the zookeeper does.

morning

afternoon

night

64 Vocabulary Practice: *zookeeper; morning, afternoon, night*
Language Practice: *feeds the monkeys, sweeps the elephant exhibit, closes the zoo*

Trace and write. Trace, read, and circle.

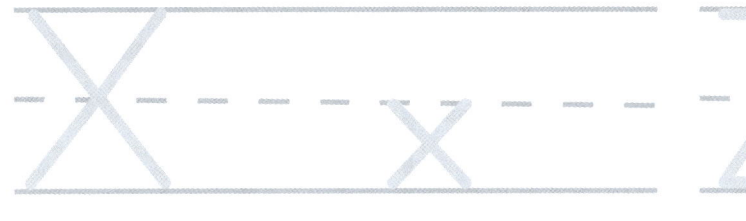

Xx   Zz

I see a zebra.

I see an ox.

I see a zoo.

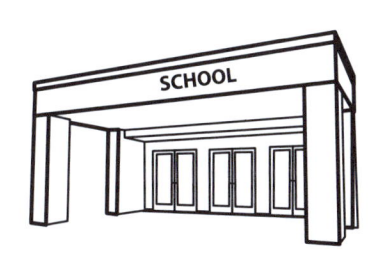

Pre-reading and Pre-writing Practice: *Xx, Zz*; simple sentences

VALUES

Who is working as a team? Color the frame. Draw.

How do you and your friends work as a team?

Values: We work as a team.

Look and listen. Draw what they see at the zoo.

At the Zoo

What do they see at the zoo?

Story Sequence: *At the Zoo*

UNIT 7

Connect the dots in number order. Name the animals.

Math Practice: *Numbers 1–90*

Circle the animals and plants that live underwater. Then draw more animals and plants and color.

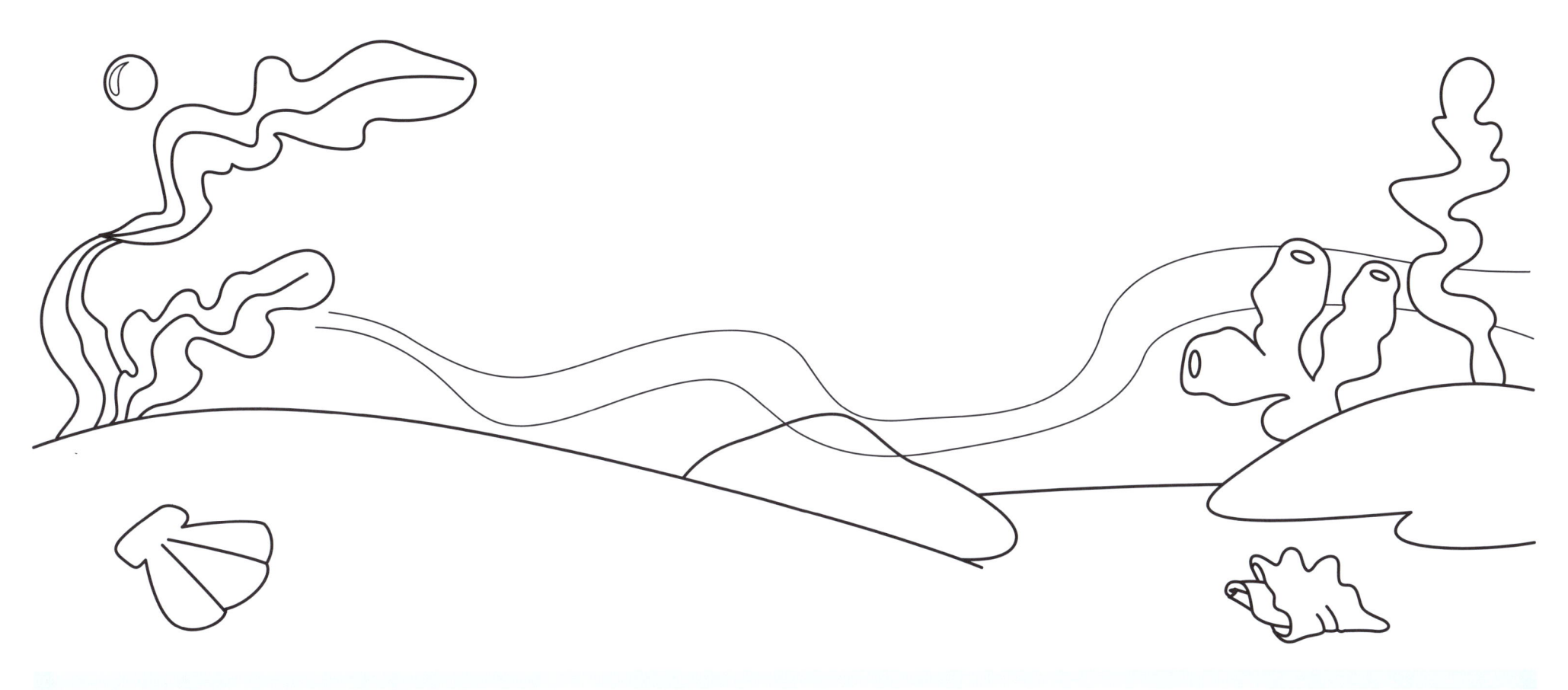

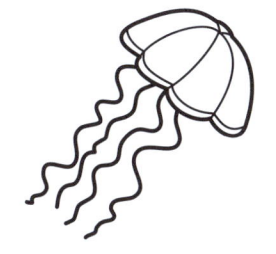

AMAZING

Amazing: Science Connection: *jellyfish, fish, coral, octopus*

UNIT 7
69

ANIMALS

Draw your favorite wild animals.

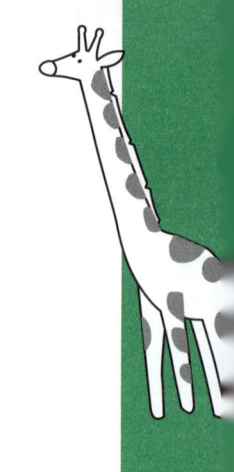

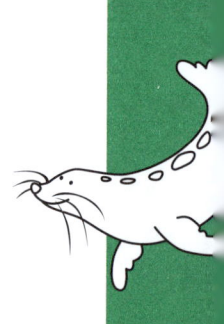

8 PLACES

What is wrong? Find and circle.

Where do you want to go? Circle. Then draw yourself in that place.

Vocabulary Practice: *beach, mountains, lake, stream*

✂ **Cut out and paste.**

Vocabulary Practice: *fishing, camping, hiking, jogging; lake, stream, mountains, beach*

UNIT 8
73

Trace, read, and match.

1 ——— first

2 ——— then

3 ——— last

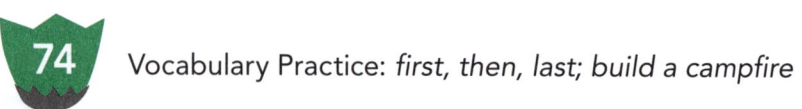

Vocabulary Practice: *first, then, last; build a campfire*

Trace and read. Look and number.

1. I see a big bird in a boat.

2. I see a big bear in a tent.

Pre-reading and Pre-writing Practice: simple sentences

VALUES

Is he sharing? Look and draw a happy or a sad face. Then draw yourself and complete the face.

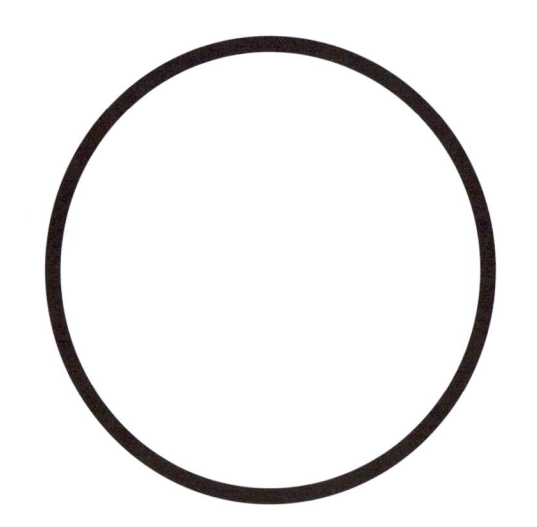

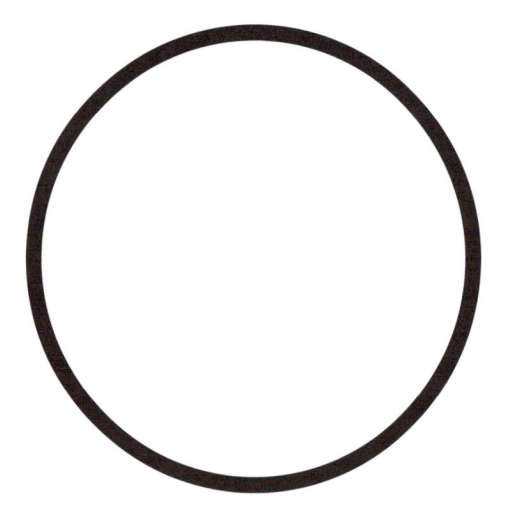

What about you?

76 Values: We share.

Look and listen. Color the animals that they see.

Camping

What do they see?

Story Sequence: *Camping*

Color the sky and write the time.

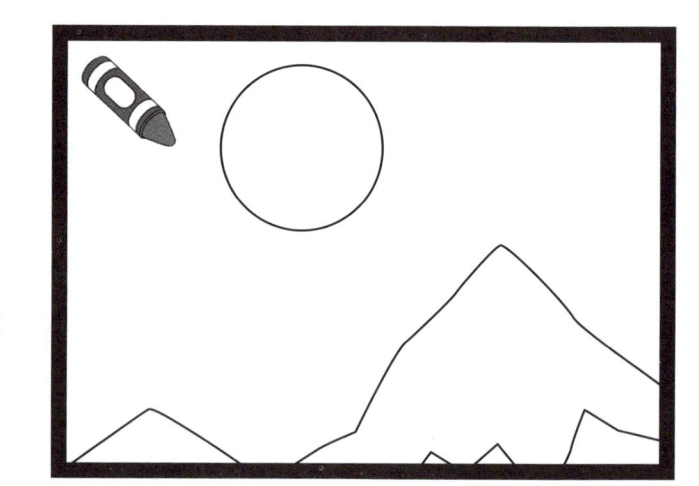

7 o'clock   12 o'clock   8 o'clock

Math Practice: *Numbers 1-12*; telling time

Trace, read, and color. Draw.

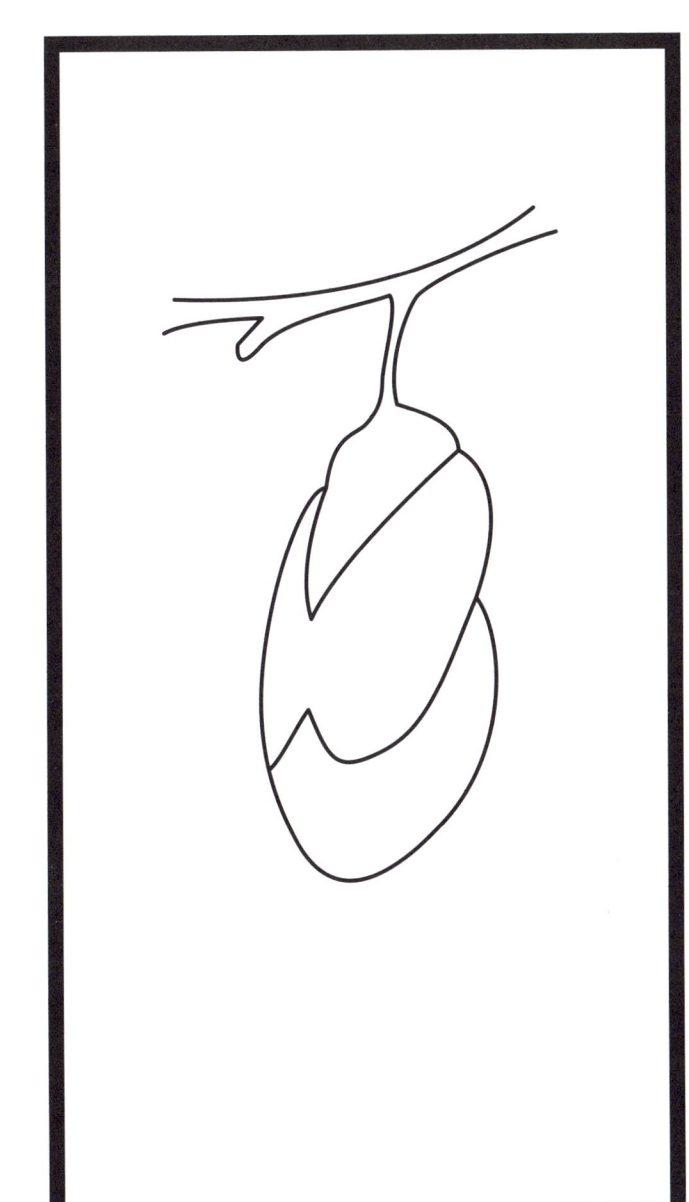

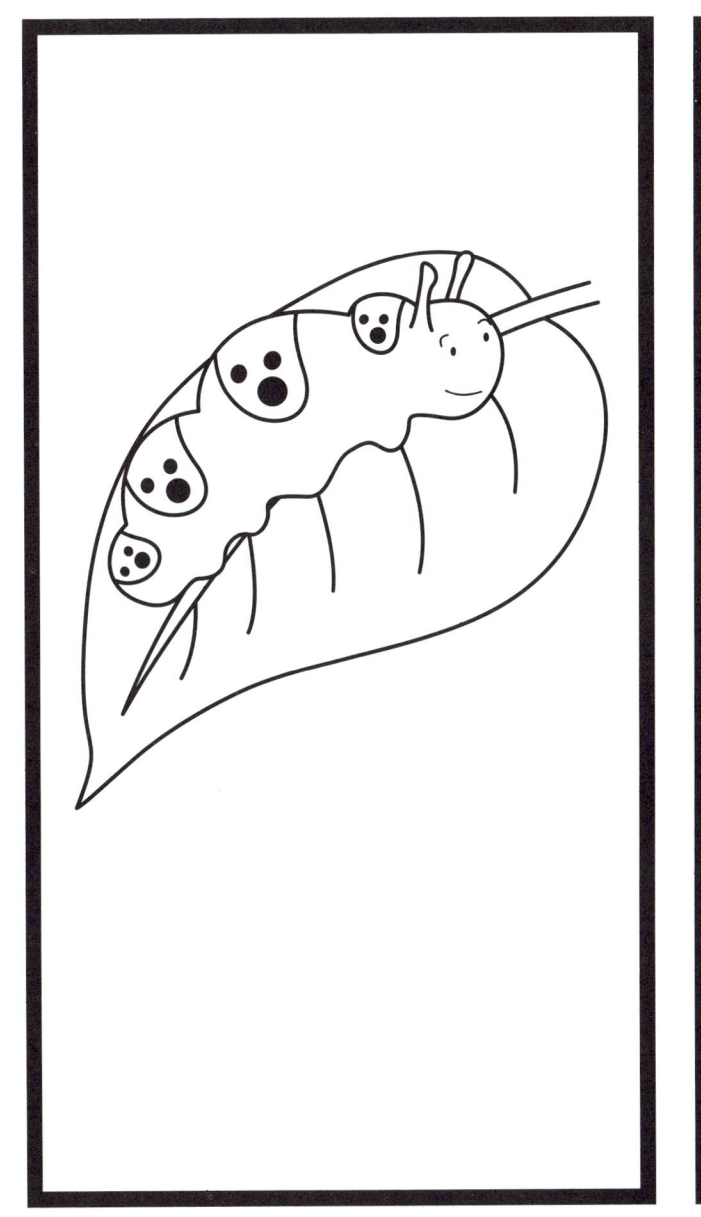

first   then   last

PLACES

Draw yourself on vacation doing your favorite activity.

9 SHOW TIME!

Look and review.

Review Units 1–8: *music teacher, sleepy, bedroom/bed, paper plate/stick/string, cake, hat/necklace, giraffes/eating, lake/fishing*

Unit 1: Look and say. Who are they? What do they do?

Unit 1: At School Assessment

Unit 2: Are you OK? Spin a crayon and say.

Unit 2: Feelings Assessment

Unit 3: Name the places in the house. What are the boy and his cat doing?

Unit 3: Home Assessment

Unit 4: Do you need… ? Spin a crayon and say.

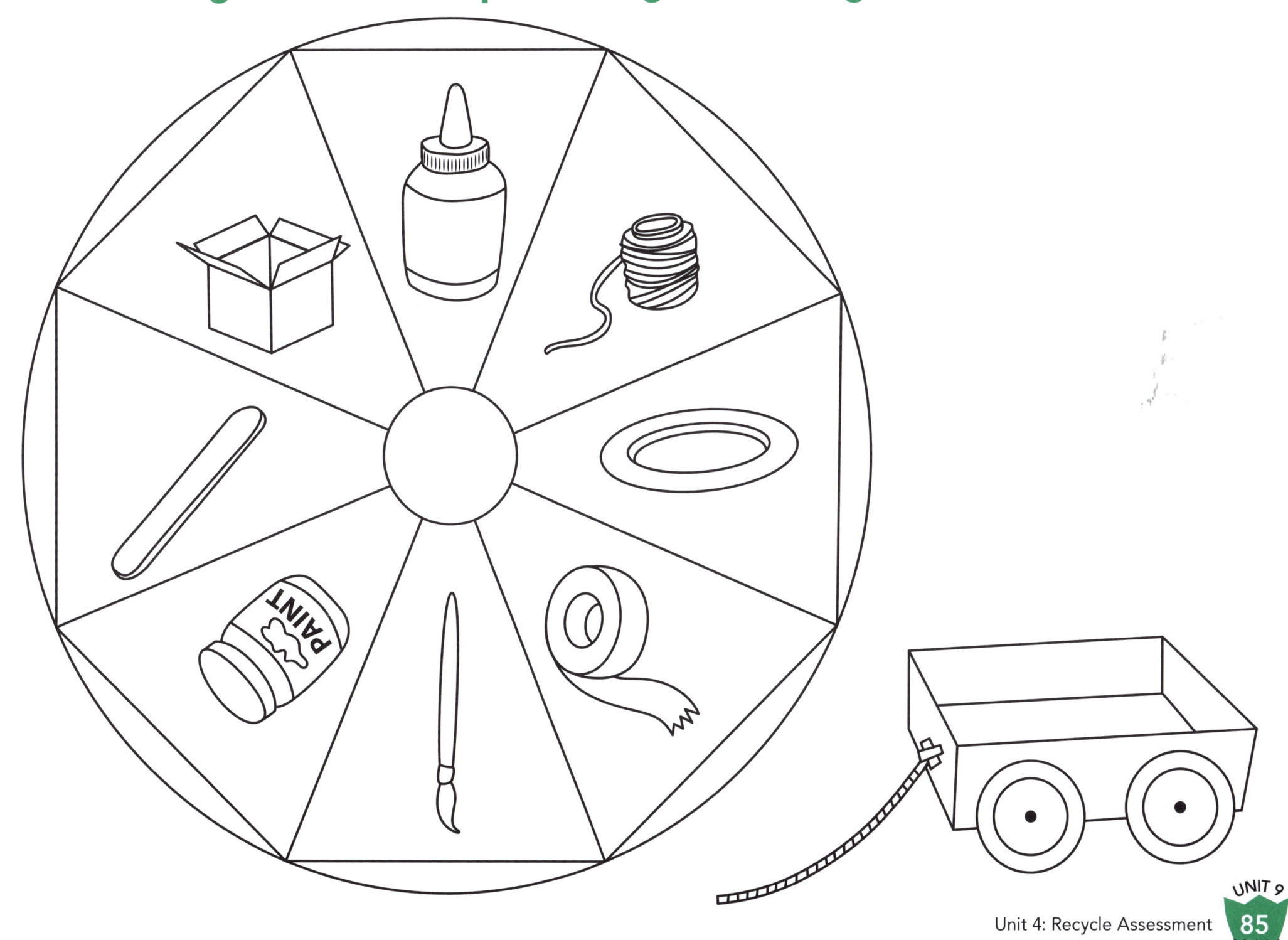

Unit 4: Recycle Assessment

Unit 5: Play the Restaurant Game. Ask politely for the items on the game board.

START

May I have _____, please.

Yes, of course.

FINISH

Unit 5: Eating Out Assessment

Unit 6: Where is the… ? Circle and say.

Unit 7: Draw your path through the zoo. What do you see? What are the animals doing? Look and say.

ENTRANCE

EXIT

Unit 7: Animals Assessment

Unit 8: Where do you want to go? What can you do there? Point and say.

Unit 8: Places Assessment

Workbook Audio CD

BIG FUN
WORKBOOK 3 AUDIO CD

TRACK	ACTIVITY
1	Copyright information
2	"Big Fun Theme Song"

Little Books
3   Unit 1 *Who Is She?*
4   Unit 2 *Are You OK?*
5   Unit 3 *Where Is Meg?*
6   Unit 4 *We Need Books!*
7   Unit 5 *Lunch with Grandma*
8   Unit 6 *At the Store*
9   Unit 7 *At the Zoo*
10   Unit 8 *Camping*

Songs and Chants
Unit 1: At School
11   "Good Morning Song"
12   "How Many Days?"
13   "Let's Have Fun"
14   "We Have Finished Chant"
15   "Good-bye Song"
16   Target Song "People at School"
17   "Values Are Important" (Part 1)
18   "Counting to 19 Chant"
19   "Amazing Nature"

Unit 2: Feelings
20   Target Song "My Feelings"
21   "Feelings Song"
22   "Let's Wiggle!"
23   "Twenties Family Chant"
24   "Shape Song"

Unit 3: Home
25   Target Song "My House"
26   "Let's Make Letters!"
27   "Thirties Family Chant"
28   "Spider Web Song"

Unit 4: Recycle
29   "Months of the Year"
30   Target Song "Recycling"
31   "Forties Family Chant"
32   "Seeds Can Travel"

Unit 5: Eating Out
33   "At the Restaurant"
34   Target Song "Eating Out"
35   "Values Are Important" (Part 2)

Unit 6: Our Things
36   "Five Fingers"
37   Target Song "My Things"
38   "My Crayon Box"
39   "Amazing Peacock"

Unit 7: Animals
40   Target Song "Animals Everywhere"
41   "Values Are Important" (Part 3)
42   "I Can Count by Tens"

Unit 8: Places
43   Target Song "Places"
44   "Weather Song"
45   "Caterpillars and Butterflies"

Unit 9: Show Time!
46   "Show Time"

red   yellow   blue   green

_____ has finished *Big Fun* **Workbook 3!**

Good job!

blue

pink

black

white

orange   purple   brown   pink